Elmo loves having
learning adventures
with his friend

_____!

Animal Alphabet

By Kara McMahon
Illustrated by Christopher Moroney

Elmo is ready to learn the Animal Alphabet, from ape to zebra! Will you help Elmo and his friends name as many animals as you can, starting with the letter **A** all the way through to **Z**?

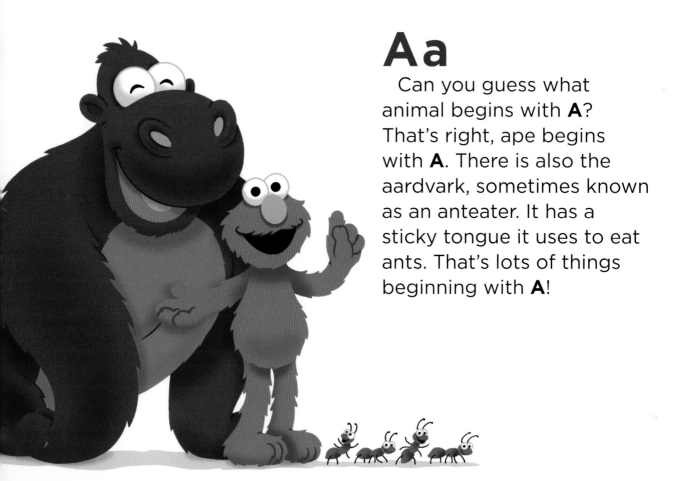

A a

Can you guess what animal begins with **A**? That's right, ape begins with **A**. There is also the aardvark, sometimes known as an anteater. It has a sticky tongue it uses to eat ants. That's lots of things beginning with **A**!

Bb

Bear begins with **B**! A bear's favorite meal is honey. And bees make honey. That's two things beginning with **B**!

Cc

Cookie Monster begins with **C**. Cookie Monster is almost as tall as a camel. Cat, canary, and camel also begin with **C**.

Dd

Barkley is a dog. Dog begins with **D**. Duck also begins with **D**. What do you do when a duck makes a splash? Duck!

Ee Ff

Ernie begins with **E**. But *he's* not an animal! Elephant begins with **E**. Ernie thinks his friend Snuffy's nose is as long as this elephant's trunk!

Fox begins with **F**. Flamingo, frog, and ferret also start with **F**.

Gg

Elmo knows some animals beginning with **G**. There are tall giraffes and tiny grasshoppers. And don't forget Dorothy, Elmo's pet goldfish!

Hh

That's a big animal with Zoe! It has a very big name, too, beginning with the letter **H**. It's a hippopotamus.

Ii Jj

Grover knows iguana starts with **I**. An iguana is a type of lizard. It has long spikes running down its back to its tail.

The jaguar is a big spotted cat. Jaguar starts with **J**. Which of these is the iguana and which is the jaguar?

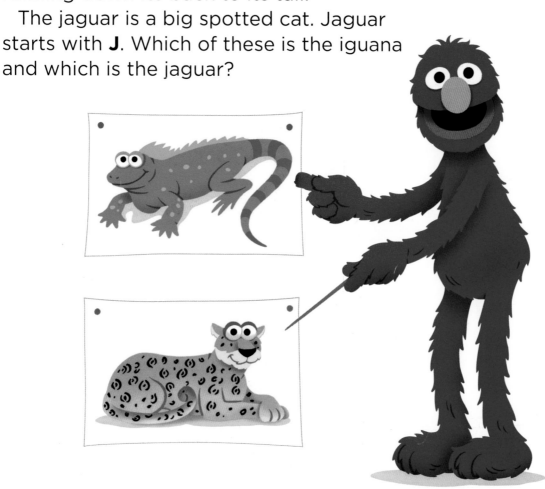

Kk

For animals beginning with **K**, Elmo hops over to Australia, where he finds a kicky kangaroo and a kindly koala.

Ll

Llama, ladybug, and lizard all begin with **L**. Which do you like a lot?

Mm

Monkey begins with **M**. Look at Elmo playing with his monkey friends. Imagine you are a monkey swinging from tree branches. What food makes a monkey go "mmmm"?

Nn Oo

Big Bird has a lot of feathered friends. Nightingale begins with **N**. Did you know that nightingales sing during the day and at night?

Owl begins with **O** and so does ostrich. Both of those are birds, too.

Pp

Bert is playing with his pet pigeon, Bernice. Pigeon begins with **P**. Pig begins with **P**, too.

Qq Rr

Quail begins with **Q**. How lucky! Because there are not many other animals that start with **Q**.

There are lots of things beginning with **R**, though. Grover is holding a rosy-nosed rabbit. Rat, reindeer, and rooster also start with **R**!

Ss

Zoe loves dancing with her animal friends beginning with **S**! Swans sail elegantly across the water, and bushy-tailed squirrels leap strongly from branch to branch. You need to be super-strong to move like that!

Tt

Toucan begins with **T**. Toucans have large beaks and live in Central America and South America. What birds live in trees near you?

Uu Vv

Elmo doesn't think there are any real animals that begin with **U**, but unicorn does. The unicorn is a make-believe animal that looks like a horse with one horn on its head.

There are not a lot of animals that start with **V**, but a vulture is one. Even though it *looks* silly, a vulture is a real bird.

W w

Worm begins with **W**. Oscar loves worms, especially his pet worm, Slimey! What else begins with **W**? Wallaby, walrus, and wolf! Can you name any others?

X x

Grover knows two animal names beginning with **X**! The xenopus is a type of frog, and there is a bird called a xenops. Extraordinary! Elmo never knew that before!

Yy Zz

You're almost through the alphabet. Can you find any animals beginning with **Y** and **Z**? Elmo knows that yak begins with **Y**! And zebra begins with **Z**! A zebra looks like a horse with black and white stripes.

Thanks for sharing this animal adventure with Elmo and his friends. You made learning the alphabet fun!

Elmo's Search Inside

Go back through the book, and see if you can find the pictures listed below.

One little ant in this book looks like it's waving hello. Can you find it?

Did you see Elmo's goldfish, Dorothy, in this book?

A baby kangaroo is called a joey. Can you find the joey in one of the pictures?

Bert loves to do "The Pigeon" with his feathered friends. Can you find the bird that's dancing along?

If there's one thing Oscar loves, it's his pet worm, Slimey. Do you see him somewhere?

Grover seems to have lost his friend the xenopus. Can you find it for him?